PROHIBIDO ENTRAR
¡No puedes ser pirata!
¡FUERA!
¡CUIDADO!

Para mi pirata favorita, CeCe, y para Jon Scieszka,
sin el que este libro no existiría – I. F.

Para Rowan y Alice, de su tía Budgie – B. B.

Puedes consultar nuestro catálogo en www.picarona.net

CÓMO SER UNA PIRATA
Texto: *Isaac Fitzgerald*
Ilustraciones: *Brigette Barrager*

1.ª edición: marzo de 2021

Título original: *How to be a pirate*

Traducción: *David Aliaga*
Maquetación: *Montse Martín*
Corrección: *Sara Moreno*



Edita: Picarona, sello infantil de Ediciones Obelisco, S. L.
Collita, 23-25. Pol. Ind. Molí de la Bastida
08191 Rubí - Barcelona
Tel. 93 309 85 25
E-mail: picarona@picarona.net

ISBN: 978-84-9145-422-9
Depósito legal: B-19.747-2020

*Printed in China*

# CÓMO SER UNA PIRATA

ISAAC FITZGERALD
BRIGETTE BARRAGER

Picarona

CeCe estaba furiosa. ¿Quiénes eran esos chicos para decirle que no podía ser una pirata? Seguro que ni siquiera habían montado en barca.

Pero CeCe conocía a alguien que...

¿Abuelo?

¡Estoy aquí,
CeCe!

—¿Cómo es ser un pirata?

—¿Y cómo iba a saber yo algo sobre eso? –preguntó el abuelo–. Pero dime, ¿por qué te interesan los piratas?

CeCe respiró hondo.

—Porque… –dijo–, los chicos dicen que son piratas y yo también quiero jugar. ¡Si hasta llevo mi espada! Pero me han dicho «Tú no puedes ser pirata»… ¿Y si tienen razón? No sé cómo ser pirata. A lo mejor tú sí que sabes. ¡Tienes un barco! Y los piratas llevan tatuajes. Así que he pensado que quizá tú lo sabrías todo sobre ellos. ¿Podrías contármelo?

—Así que quieres saber cosas sobre piratas, ¿eh? –preguntó el abuelo–. Bien, creo que la primera cosa que un pirata tiene que ser es...

# ¡VALIENTE!

Un pirata va en busca de la aventura
y no tiene miedo a los obstáculos.

—¿Qué más? –preguntó CeCe.

—Tiene que ser...

# ¡RÁPIDO!

Un pirata está listo para
actuar ante el peligro
en cualquier momento.

¡Eeeeee!

—¿Otra cosa más? –preguntó CeCe.

—No todo tiene que ver con
el peligro... —susurró el abuelo—.
Un pirata sabe cuándo tiene que...

¡DIVERTIRSE!

¡Oleeee!

—¡Más! –exclamó CeCe.

—Otra cosa que tiene
que ser un pirata es...

# ¡INDEPENDIENTE!

Tener una buena tripulación es importante, pero, al final, un pirata debe afrontar sus problemas por sí mismo.

¡Yujuuuu!

—¿Pero sabes qué es lo más importante para un pirata? –preguntó el abuelo–. Es algo incluso más importante que ser valiente o rápido, que saber cuándo divertirse o incluso que ser independiente...

—¿Un tesoro? –preguntó CeCe–. ¿Cañones?

—Lo más importante que debe tener una persona, ya sea un pirata o no, es...

¡AMOR!

CECE

CeCe corrió con los pies ligeros y el corazón fuerte.

PROHIBIDO ENTRAR
¡FUERA!
¡CUIDADO!

¡Soy valiente!
¡Soy rápida!
¡Soy independiente!
¡Y me estoy
divirtiendo!

¡Me ENCANTA ser una pirata!

# Flip the Flaps Planet Earth

Dr Mike Goldsmith and Nicki Palin

First published 2010 by Kingfisher
This edition published 2012 by Kingfisher
an imprint of Macmillan Children's Books
a division of Macmillan Publishers Limited
20 New Wharf Road, London N1 9RR
Basingstoke and Oxford
Associated companies throughout the world
www.panmacmillan.com

Consultant: Professor Robert Francis

ISBN 978-0-7534-3462-8



1 3 5 7 9 8 6 4 2
1TR/0911/UNTD/LFA/157MA

A CIP catalogue record for this book is available from the British Library.

Printed in China

# Contents

# Planet Earth

The Earth is where we live, a planet that spins through space. If you flew to the Moon in a rocket, you would see the Earth in the sky, like a huge, bright disc coloured blue and white.

**1.** A planet is a huge ball of rock or gas that moves around the Sun.

**2.** Yes. The Earth spins round once a day.

**3.** At night, the Sun shines on the other side of the Earth. So it is day there when it is night where you are.

**The path of the Earth**

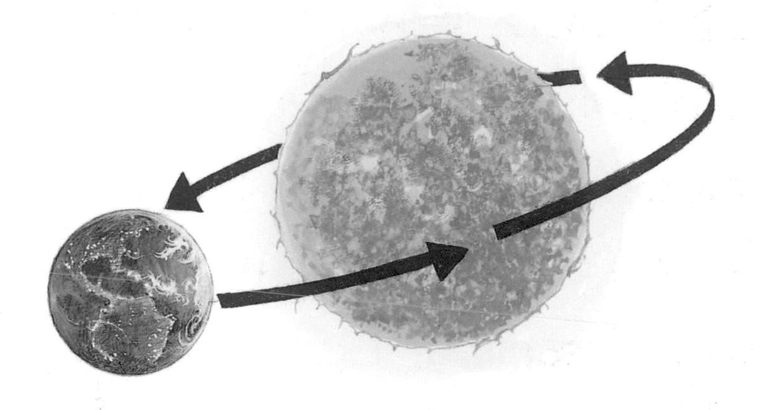

It takes a year for the Earth to go once around the Sun.

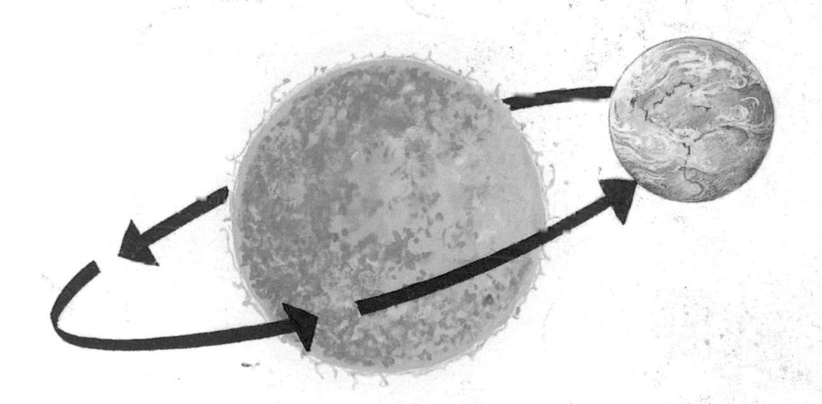

After six months, the Earth has gone half-way round.

# Air

The air is all around us. We need air to breathe. Clouds float in it, birds fly in it, and we call it wind when it moves.

**1.** Air is a mixture of gases. Oxygen is one of these gases, which we need to breathe.

**2.** The atmosphere is the layer of air that covers the Earth like a blanket.

**3.** No. The atmosphere fades away the higher up it goes. There is no air at all a few kilometres above the Earth.

**People climbing high mountains take air with them to breathe.**

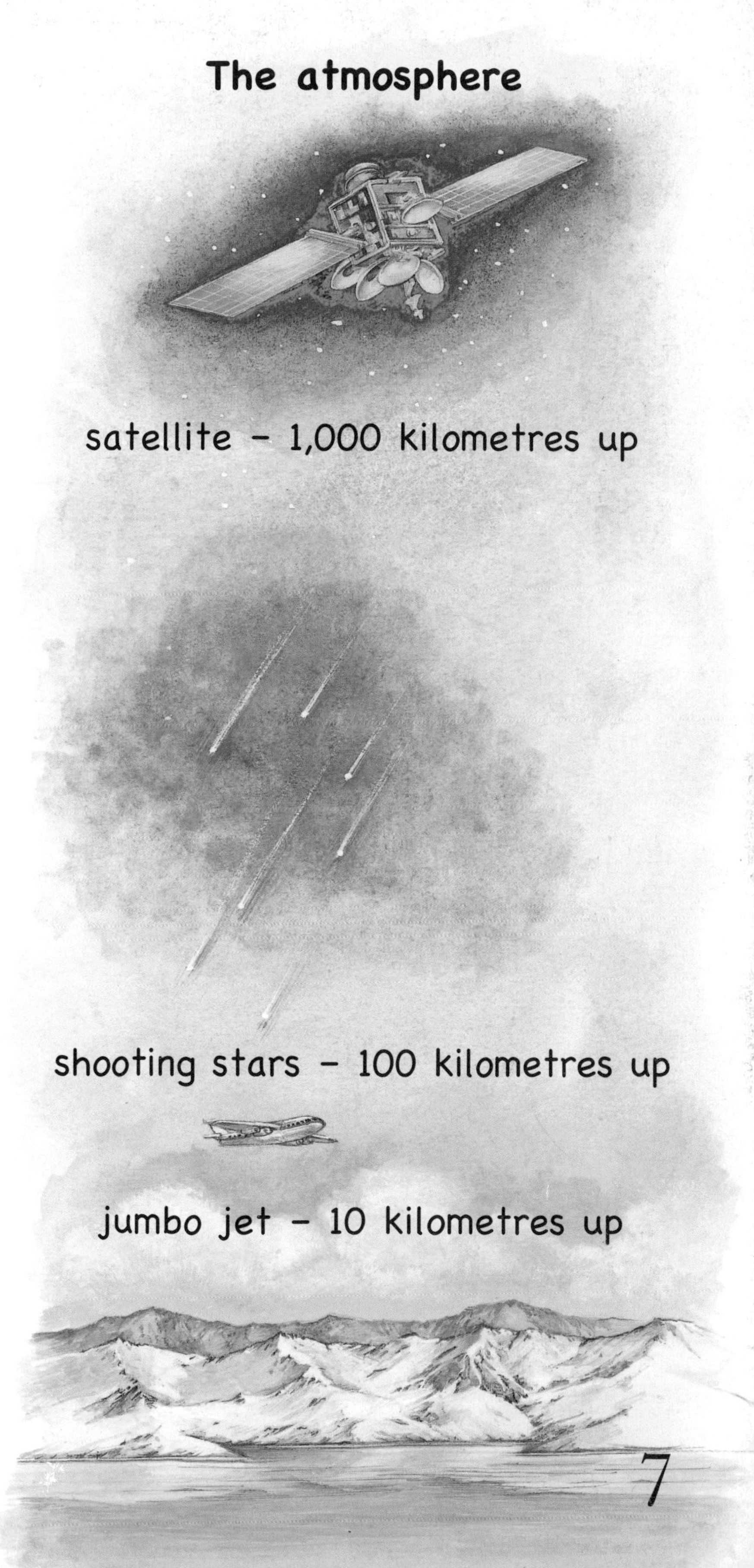

# Life on Earth

Planet Earth is full of life because there is air and water here. Fish swim in the oceans, birds swoop through the air, and many other animals run on the ground, or burrow beneath it.

**1.** Yes. There are things living in the deepest oceans, the highest mountains, and even the hottest and coldest places on Earth.

**2.** Yes. Plants live and grow – and they breathe, too!

**3.** The blue whale is the largest animal on Earth. It's as heavy as 2,500 people!

**There are many types of life on Earth.**

toadstools

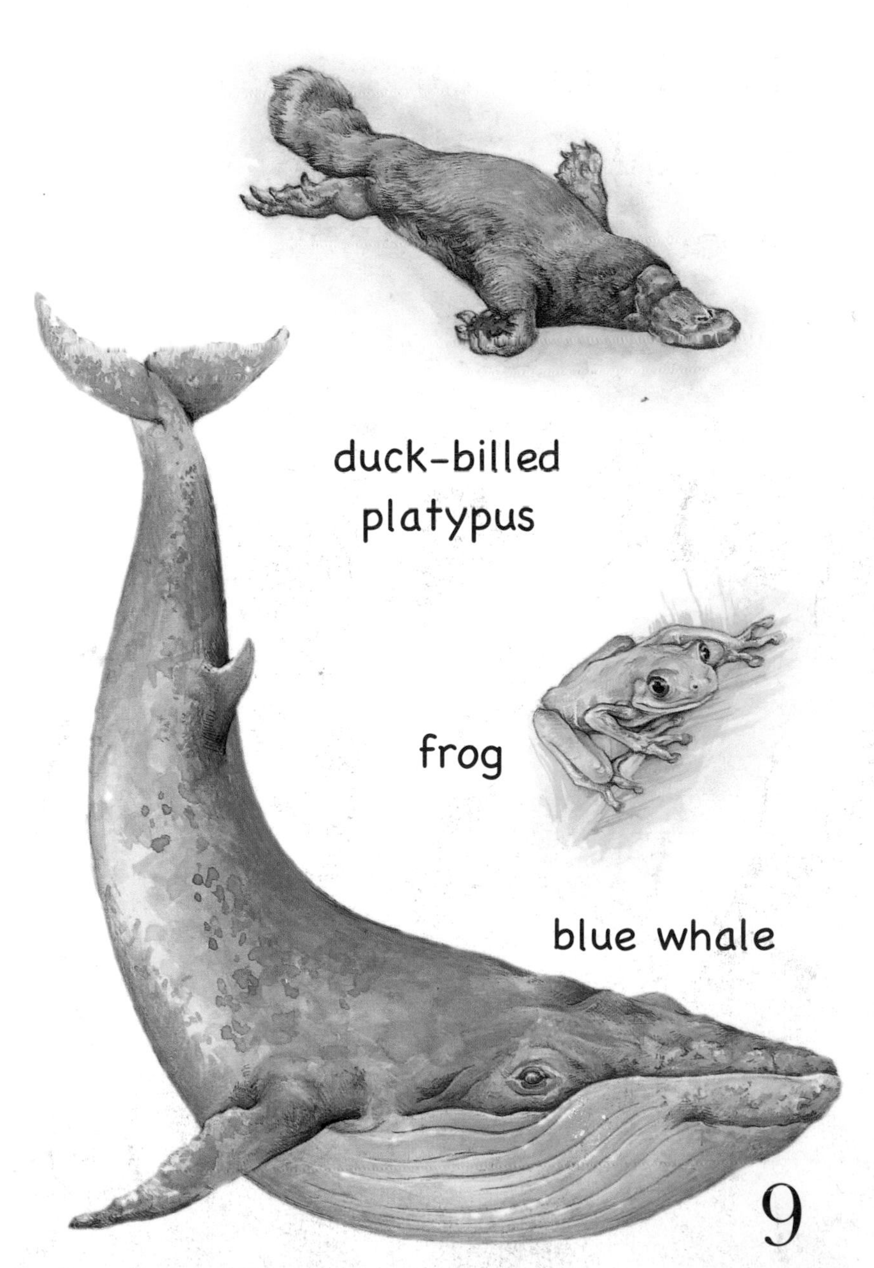

duck-billed platypus

frog

blue whale

# The oceans

Most of Earth is covered in blue oceans of salty water, full of fish and other living things. In some places, the water is frozen into shining white ice.

**1.** There are five oceans. They are called the Arctic, Atlantic, Indian, Pacific and Southern oceans.

**2.** The ocean has a floor, with mountains and valleys.

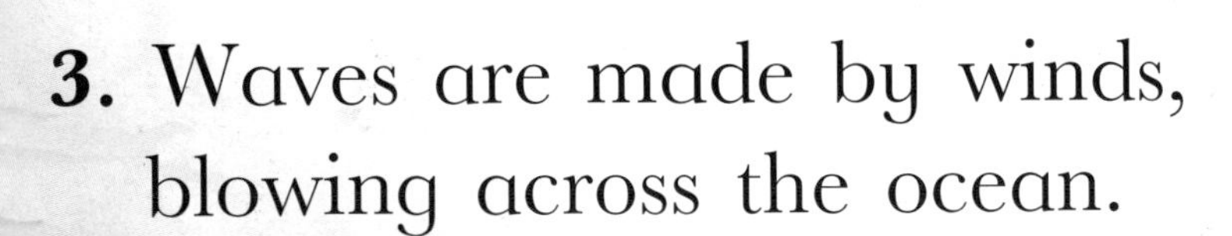

**3.** Waves are made by winds, blowing across the ocean.

## Life in the ocean

turtle

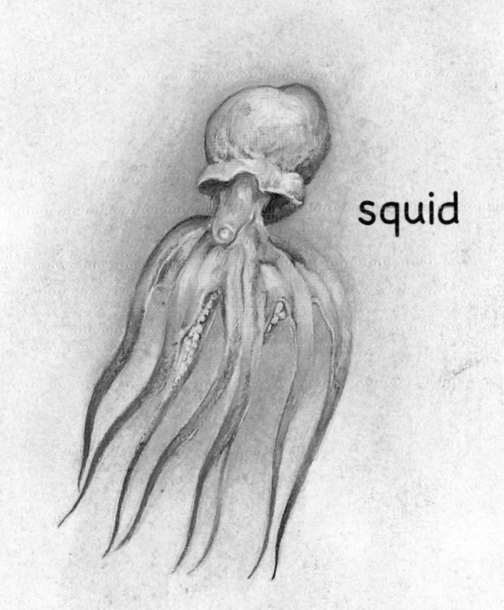

squid

deep-sea anglerfish

# Inside our planet

If you dug a hole under your house, you might find many things: soil or concrete... even tunnels or caves! But under this, inside the Earth, you would soon reach a thick layer of solid rock.

**one side of the Earth**

**1.** No. The deeper you go underground, the hotter it gets.

**2.** Deep underground it is so hot that the rocks melt and become liquid.

**3.** There is a huge ball of metal, called the core, in the middle of the Earth.

**Inside Earth's surface layer**

plant roots and a water pipe

ancient ruins

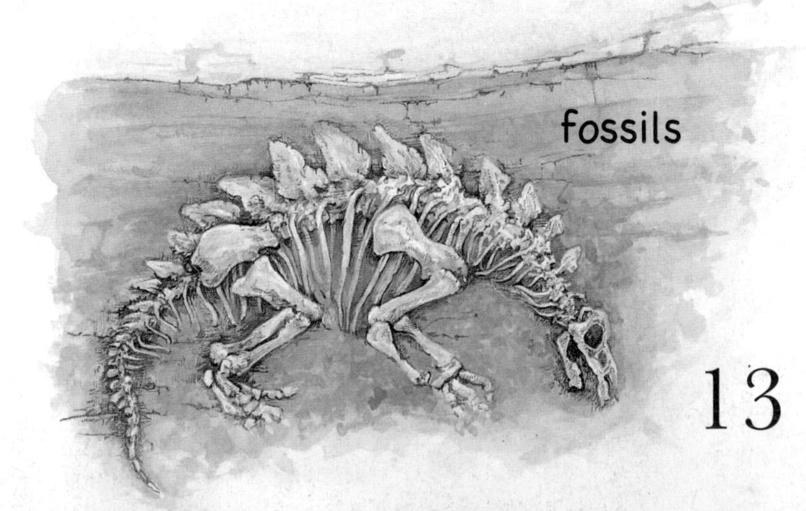

fossils

# Earthquakes

Sometimes the earth shakes and trembles, and huge cracks may appear in the ground. Buildings crack and crumble, and some fall down. This is an earthquake.

**1.** Deep underground, huge pieces of rock scrape slowly past each other. Sometimes, they slip suddenly, making the land above them shake.

**2.** 'Quake' is another word for 'shake'.

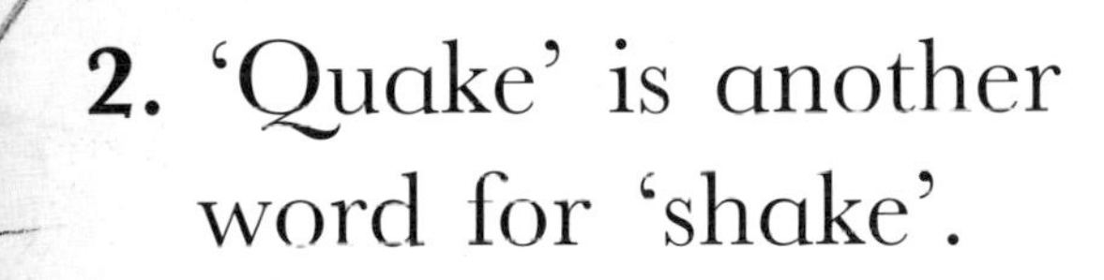

**3.** No, but we can make buildings that do not fall down when an earthquake happens.

## Why the ground shakes

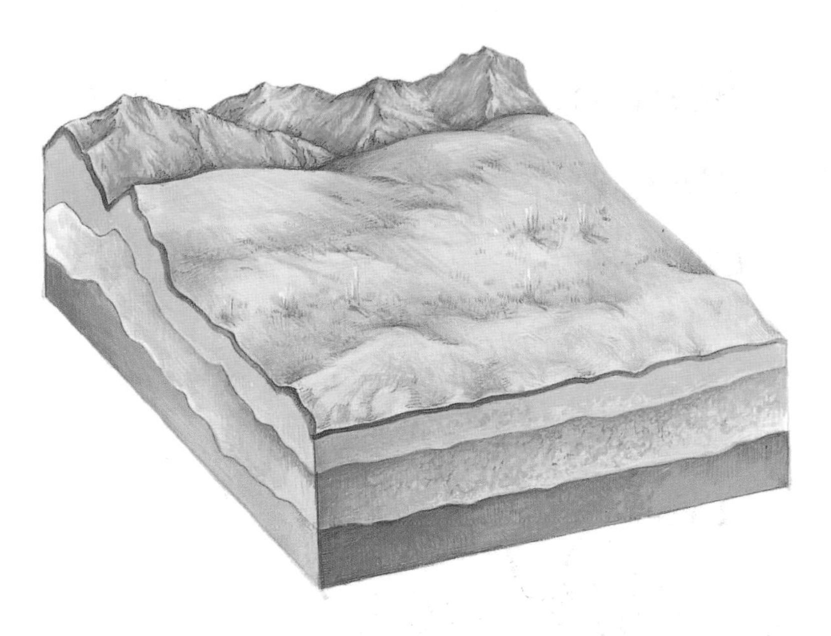

Most of the time, the rocky plates below Earth's surface move slowly...

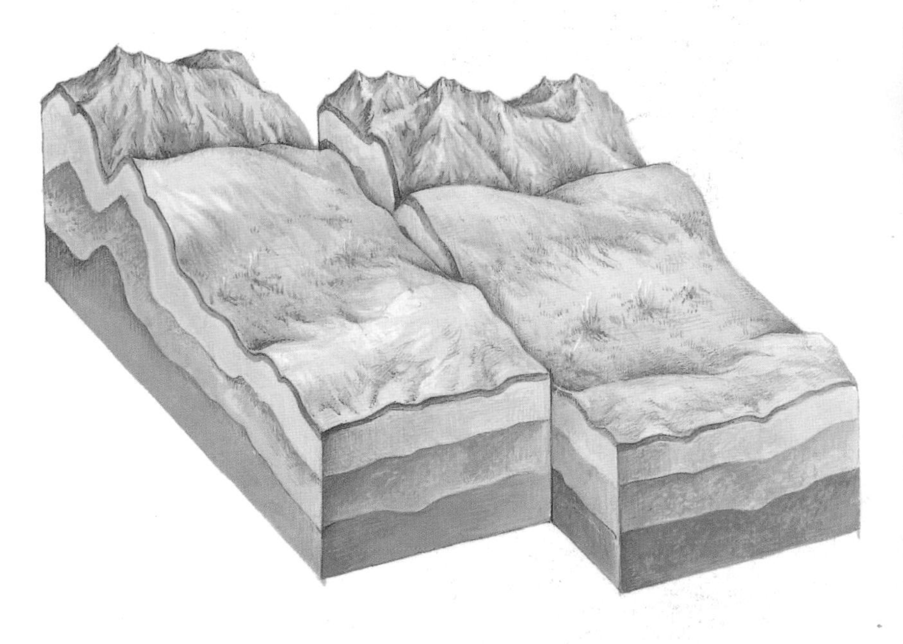

...but sometimes, they suddenly slip.

# Volcanoes

Not all mountains are quiet and still. Some of them can throw out smoke and fire, like huge fireworks! Mountains like this are called volcanoes.

**1.** Lava is very hot liquid rock from deep inside the Earth. It sometimes flows out of volcanoes.

**2.** No. Volcanoes are found only in some parts of the world.

**3.** Yes. Sometimes the lava from these volcanoes turns into new islands.

**An island is formed**

underwater volcano erupts

volcano grows larger

volcano cools and plants appear

a new island has formed

# Index